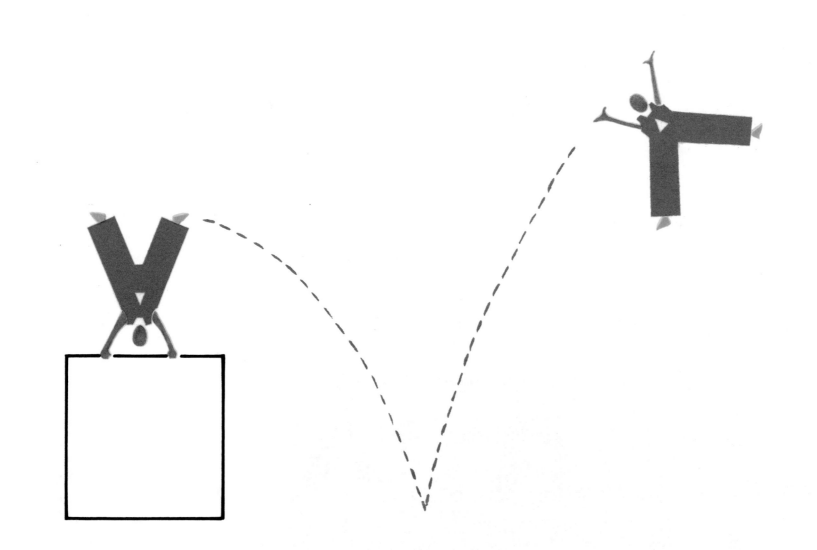

ALPHABATICS

Suse MacDonald

A TRUMPET CLUB SPECIAL EDITION

Aa

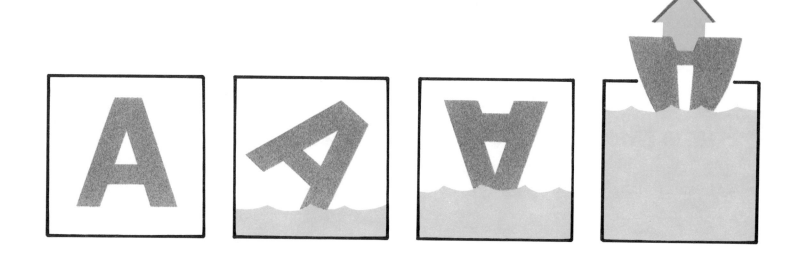

Ark

Bb

balloon

Cc

Clown

Dd

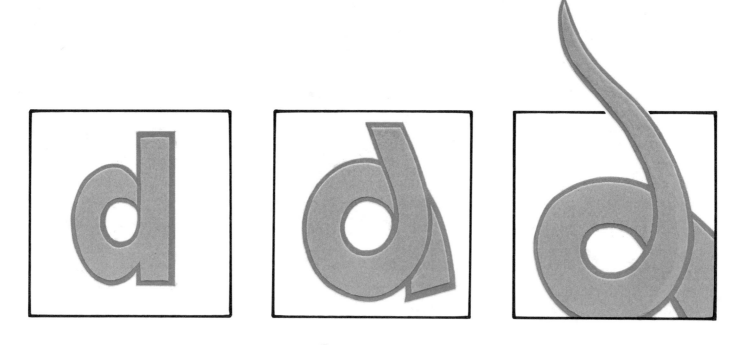

dragon

Ee

Ff

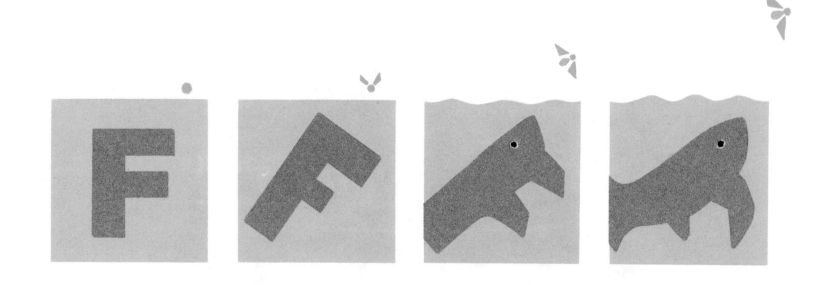

Fish

Gg

Giraffe

Hh

house

insect

Jj

jack-in-the-box

Kk

K

Kite

Ll

Lion

Mm

mustache

Nn

nest

owl

Plane

Qq

Quail

Rr

rooster

Ss

Swan

Tt

Tree

Uu

umbrella

Vv

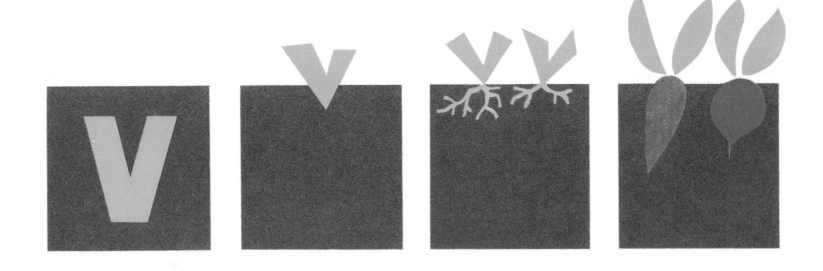

Vegetables

Ww

Whale

Xx

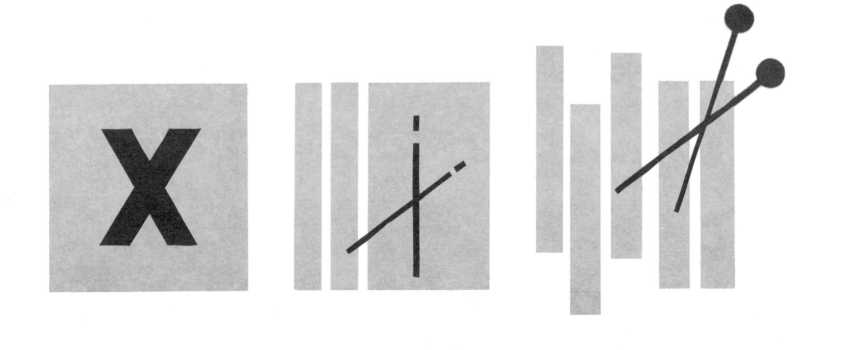

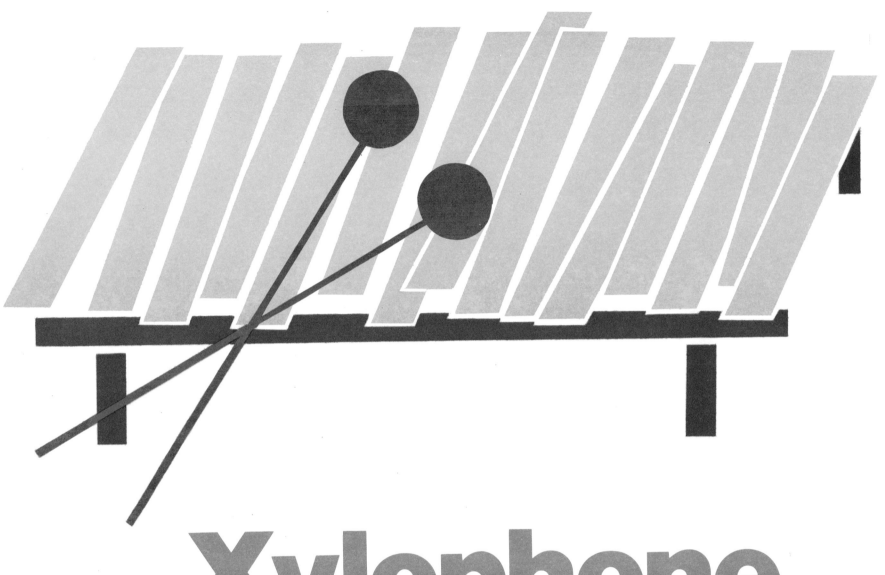

Xylophone

Yy

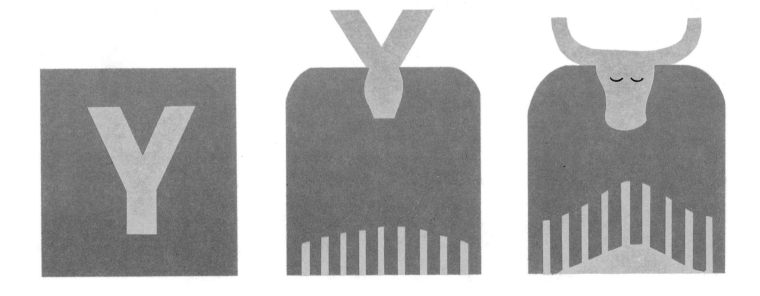

Yak

Z z

Zebra

For Stuart, with special thanks to Susan and Deborah

ISBN 0-590-97933-7

12 11 10 9 8 7 6 5 4   6 7 8 9/9 0 1/0

Printed in the U.S.A.